JOSEPH LISTER

JOSEPH LISTER, 1869

JOSEPH LISTER

Father of Modern Surgery

by

RHODA TRUAX

WITH A FOREWORD BY

LORD HORDER G.C.V.O. M.D. F.R.C.P.
Physician in Ordinary to H.M. the King

WITH TEN ILLUSTRATIONS IN HALF-TONE

GEORGE G. Harrap & CO. LTD.
LONDON   SYDNEY   TORONTO   BOMBAY

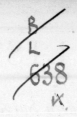

First published 1947
by GEORGE G. HARRAP & CO. LTD.
182 High Holborn, London, W.C.1

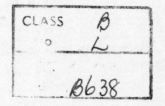

*Composed in Baskerville type and printed by Western Printing Services, Ltd.,
Bristol. Made in Great Britain.*

Foreword

In the field of Science chance only favours the mind that is prepared. -

LOUIS PASTEUR

SURGERY, AS PRACTISED TO-DAY, HAS become such a familiar experience in the life of the community that it is difficult to realize that it is the result of a rapid evolution during only two generations of doctors. Up till the middle of the last century the whole field of surgery was severely limited by three great obstacles—pain, hæmorrhage, and sepsis. The discovery and exploitation of anæsthetics removed the first handicap; the introduction of the ligature, and especially of the absorbable ligature, greatly diminished the second. The elimination of the third great obstacle to surgery, sepsis of the tissues about the wound, or 'putrefaction,' as it was formerly termed, was a much slower business. It did not depend upon a chemical or a physical discovery; it was the result of a patient and persistent pursuit of an idea born and bred in the mind of Joseph Lister. Inasmuch as the surgery of to-day is the child of his conception that sepsis results from contamination of tissues exposed by the surgeon's knife by living microbes—and this conception lay at the root of all his painstaking work throughout a long and epoch-marking life—Lister has been justly called the "Father of Modern Surgery."

To the genius of one man more than any other Lister owed a tremendous stimulus in the pursuit of his investigations and in the confirmation of his views. This was Louis Pasteur, with whom over many years he corresponded freely. Pasteur's experiments and discoveries formed an ultimate basis for, and a justification of, Lister's efforts. The cordiality of the relations between the two men, and their mutual respect and affection, provide a unique chapter in the history of medical science and of humanism.

5

The older surgeons achieved a degree of rapidity and dexterity in their work which was quite amazing. These qualities
attracted and fascinated the students who thronged the
operating-theatres where Cheselden, Syme, and others like
them performed feats which rendered them famous. The
introduction of anæsthetics and the control of hæmorrhage
gave the surgeon time for more deliberate action; the slower
evolution of the defences against wound-infection (sepsis) not
only extended the time available for an already familiar
operation, but made possible other procedures which could
not even be attempted when time was severely limited. The
abdomen could be opened with less risk of peritonitis, the
era of thoracic surgery—formerly almost confined to the
simple draining of abscesses—began, and the same thing took
place in regard to the brain. Delicate operations upon the
eye were made possible. Joints were opened and closed again
without fear of their becoming fixed by inflammation.
Severed nerves were joined together without the produc-
tion of massive adhesions rendering the end-result ineffective.

These new fields gave great scope for the development of
craftsmanship in surgery, with skilful technique gradually
replacing legerdemain. At one time there was perhaps a
danger lest deliberation should become excessive, the surgeon losing his awareness of how time passed, so spoilt,
almost, had he become as the result of the rapidly improving
art of the anæsthetist and the lowered mortality following
carefully planned procedures.

Even Lister himself was adversely criticized because he
took some time over his operations; he was already 'cashing
in' on the added security against wound-infection given by
the implementation of his principle. His more studied care
of the tissues dealt with and of the bleeding-points, though
greatly in the patient's interest, must have contrasted
strongly with the lightning speed of the surgeons of the
older school. This probably led, at least in part, to the
notion that Lister was not a very brilliant surgeon, as such.
But the 'proof of the pudding' was, once again, 'in the eat-

ing'—that is to say, the mortality rate decided, in no uncertain manner, which was the better method.

Not only were new fields entered, but new techniques were invented, and a whole series of new instruments by which these techniques might be carried out. Backed by greater security against shock and sepsis, the ambitious mind of the modern surgeon has surveyed every branch of medicine and has staked out a claim as wide as pathology itself—a claim that has justified itself again and again. He no longer deals only with the gross effects of trauma, with tumours, with acute inflammatory crises, and with the end-results of pathological processes; he is also the close ally of the physician in taking steps to arrest, in their earlier stages, many diseases which, not amenable to medical measures, or only amenable when these include the imposition of a prolonged and serious restriction upon normal activity, pursue a progressively disabling course. The successful correction of more and more types of deformity has led by natural steps to the wide range of operations classed as plastic surgery—a range that is extending every year. Perhaps the latest and most significant example in this field is the grafting into the body of living tissues whose internal secretions are essential to life and giving them a blood-supply to enable them to function.

Only when complete freedom from sepsis is secured can these modern surgical procedures succeed or even be contemplated. I spoke just now of the slowness of the evolution of the defences against sepsis. The first great step was the discovery by Semmelweis that 'surgical cleanliness' was a factor of great importance in the preventive treatment of puerperal fever, and the realization that there was an affinity between this disease and the pyæmia, or generalized sepsis, which so often followed wound-infection.

Then came the antiseptic method of Lister. And after that, by a material development of Lister's original conception, the aseptic school, with which the name of Von Bergman is so closely associated. It is the aseptic principle that holds the field to-day. The whole lay-out of the modern operating-theatre is based upon this principle. That is the meaning of the special construction of the room—the sterilized dressings, sponges, pads, and instruments; the surgeons', anæsthetists', and nurses' caps and masks; the silence imposed upon everybody present. This meticulous attention to detail is not, even yet, a uniform custom. Intelligence, discipline, and team-work are necessary for the full implementation of the principle. The absence of these may lead to dangerous anomalies: here one sees a nurse's forelock uncovered; there one hears the surgeon recounting his experiences to his assistant, not realizing that most gauze shields to the mouth are not impervious to droplet infection during talking; in still another place a coil of bowel lies exposed and uncovered by the protecting pad, or a forgotten 'retractor' exercises pressure on the edge of the wound for an unduly lengthy period. Respect for the ubiquity of the offending microbe and a minimum of damage to the parts that are to heal become essential and conditioned elements in a surgeon's facility and are reflected in his results. Also essential, and as much to-day as formerly, are his dexterity and his sense of time. The best teaching he gives his pupils is the demonstration of his own methods in the daily course of his work.

In view of all that I have said we may surely welcome an edition of Rhoda Truax's biography of Joseph Lister in the country that boasts his birth and his life's work. In this book will be found a very readable account of Lister's unique contribution to surgery, and also a fascinating story of his life. If history is made up of the lives of great men here is a chapter of history which all should read. Of the lives and deeds of the great killers through the ages—of Alexander and Cæsar and Napoleon—we have many. Here is the life of a great saviour of mankind. It is surely a fitting accompaniment to the thought and proclaimed intention of to-day, when to preserve and to increase the value of human life, rather than to destroy and to degrade it, are in the minds of every intelligent citizen.

HORDER

Contents

Illustrations

*The illustrations except the frontispiece
will be found between pages 32 and 33*

Rab and His Friends

ONE FINE LATE OCTOBER AFTERNOON
in 1830 a huge mastiff sauntered into the courtyard of Minto
House Hospital, as though he were "taking general posses-
sion of the place; like the Duke of Wellington entering a
subdued city, satiated with victory and peace." Behind him
came his master, James the Howgate carrier, leading his
mare, and in the cart was a beautiful old woman, James's
wife. The old man helped her alight. "Had Solomon, in all
his glory, been handing down the Queen of Sheba at his
palace gate, he could not have done it more daintily, more
tenderly, more like a gentleman, than did James the Howgate carrier, when he lifted down Ailie, his wife."

John Brown, a clerk serving his apprenticeship to James
Syme, the well-known Edinburgh surgeon, happened to be
in the courtyard when the procession entered. He and the
carrier had known each other for half a dozen years,
having met through the heroic dog to whom Brown had
become very much attached. "Rab had the dignity and
simplicity of great size, . . . the gravity of all great fighters,"
he said later, when he was telling the story. "I wish you
could have seen him. There are no such dogs now. He
belonged to a lost tribe."

Now, in tragic circumstances, John Brown met Rab's
mistress, the old woman whom her husband treated like a
queen.

Young Brown examined her. So did James Syme, who
confirmed Brown's fears; only an operation could possibly
save Ailie's life.

And so the operation was performed—without an anæs-
thetic, for ether was not to be used for another sixteen years.
Ailie bore it bravely. James and Rab witnessed the operation,

13

James sitting apart, with Rab's huge and noble head between his knees. Then Ailie was put to bed, and James stayed by her side, for he wanted no one else to care for her. "I'll be her nurse," he said, "and I'll gang aboot on my stockin' soles as canny as pussy."

At first Ailie did well. "But four days after the operation she had a sudden and long shivering, a 'groosin' she called it. . . . Her eyes were too bright, her cheek coloured . . . the balance was lost, the mischief had begun. On looking at the wound, a blush of red told the secret."

The young clerk knew only too well what the blush of red and the shivering meant: pyæmia—wound-infection, the scourge of surgery. Nothing could be done but to let the disease run its course; after days of delirium and suffering Ailie quietly died.

The huge dog guarded her bed while James went out into the darkness and the November snow, returning with his old mare and the cart. He took his wife in his arms, "and with a resolved but utterly miserable face, strode along the passage. . . . I heard the solitary cart sound through the streets, and die away, and come again. . . .

"James buried his wife, with his neighbours mourning, Rab inspecting the solemnity from a distance. . . . Then [James] rather suddenly fell ill, and took to bed; was insensible when the doctor came, and soon died. . . . The grave was not difficult to reopen."

The old dog slunk home to the stable, where he refused food and prevented the mare from being fed. Reluctantly the new carrier had to kill him. "I was laith to make awa' wi' the auld dowg, his like wasna atween this and Thornhill," he told the clerk apologetically, "but 'deed, sir, I could do naething else."

The clerk believed him. It was a fit end for an old dog whose friends were gone.

That was the story of "The Howgate Carrier, his Wife, and his Dog Rab" as the young clerk used to tell it. Later he became Dr John Brown, well-known medical and literary

man, friend of Ruskin, Thackeray, and Mark Twain; and his little story was published under the title of *Rab and his Friends*. Countless numbers of people cried over it, moved by what the poet Swinburne referred to as Dr Brown's "love of children and the dead."

But though they cried over Ailie and James and Rab, they did not question the inevitability of her death. They did not ask themselves, "Why did Ailie have to die?" That, they knew, was to be expected when people were operated on. In those days entering a surgical hospital was often the equivalent of signing one's death-warrant.

The man who changed all that was born three years before Ailie died, the son of a Quaker couple named Isabella and Joseph Jackson Lister. He too was touched by the story of the old woman, but he did more than sympathize; he resolved not to rest until he had eliminated the disease which caused her death.

It was a tremendous task. Something like half the patients operated on in hospitals inevitably died, usually from septic diseases. This was true despite the fact that only the simplest surgical procedures were attempted, few surgeons being reckless enough to operate upon the chest, abdomen, or brain. Compound fractures—fractures in which there was an external wound leading to the break in the bone—usually meant that the limb had to be amputated, and thus accounted for a large number of the deaths. If an epidemic of gangrene or some other hospital disease broke out the mortality soared, and not half but all of the patients in an infected ward might die.

That was the way things were when Ailie entered Minto House Hospital—and for many years afterwards. Surgeons had become excellent craftsmen, operating rapidly and with great technical skill, but surgery itself was closer to its primitive state than to the science it has become to-day.

By asking why Ailie had to die, and finding the answer to that question, Joseph Lister defeated an enemy so powerful that no operation, no matter how simple, was considered

safe. Within a few years after Lister's discovery five times as many operations were performed, many of them procedures no one had dared to attempt before, and the mortality dropped to one-tenth of what it had been. For about a hundred years before Lister practically every mother undergoing a Cæsarean section died; immediately afterwards only one in ten failed to survive, then one in every twenty, until to-day the operation only rarely causes the death of a healthy woman.

During the American Civil War the number of soldiers who died of wound-infection was so great that figures are almost unobtainable. As Major Albert Gaillard Hart, a Union surgeon, put it, "What we term pyæmia or blood-poisoning has always been the scourge of armies, and ours was no exception. At the field hospital the cases were very frequent. Statistics are unnecessary; they proved uniformly fatal." Now all of that is changed. Blood-poisoning is no longer a scourge, and 97·5 per cent. of the men wounded in battle recover. Perhaps even more important is the fact that the overwhelming majority of these men are able to lead normal, useful lives, whereas the few Civil War casualties who did survive were usually helpless invalids and cripples.

It is actually not strange that Lister is not better known, for few great doctors achieve the popularity of heroes from other walks of life. Compared with other doctors, the name of Lister is by no means obscure; it has a more familiar ring than those of John Hunter, Ignaz Semmelweis, Rudolf Virchow, or Robert Koch. If it is less familiar than such names as Newton, Faraday, Darwin, and Curie, we must remember that the history of medicine is not taught anywhere except in a few medical schools: it is supposed to be interesting and valuable only to certain physicians.

It is only very recently that people have begun to realize that discoveries which have increased their chances of living are just as interesting as those which may cause their death. The number of people who visited the Wellcome Historical Medical Museum in London—where the wards in which

Lister worked his miracle have been reproduced and his instruments and apparatus preserved—is very small compared with the numbers which flock to visit exhibitions of military weapons.

There is another reason why so little is known about Joseph Lister, in spite of the many honours which were heaped upon him, and that was his own modesty. By keeping his own remarkable personality as far out of the limelight as he could he made his work seem almost anonymous. The very magnitude of his discovery, which opened the way to so many other discoveries, helped to create this anonymity. People readily assumed that anything so important must have happened long ago. It is, indeed, difficult to realize that men and women are living to-day who read the story of Ailie and took it for granted that infection must follow the surgeon's knife.

This book, then, attempts to describe Lister's work, the birth of modern surgery and its rapid development during his long and active life. And, in addition, it attempts to tell the personal story of Joseph Lister, the story of a man and of the woman he so deeply loved.

B

CHAPTER I

The Godless College

Wʜᴇɴ Jᴏsᴇᴘʜ Lɪsᴛᴇʀ's ғᴀᴛʜᴇʀ ᴡᴀs about ten years old an incident occurred which, trivial as it seemed at the time, had a lasting effect upon him and, indirectly, on the Lister family.

The boy had been writing in his copybook, and while he was waiting for his father to inspect his lesson he happened to look out of the window. It was then that he made a remarkable discovery. Due to a defect in the glass, a kind of bubble had been formed, and when he looked through the bubble he could see everything outside much more clearly than he could when he looked through the rest of the pane, or even when the window was open.

Just then the boy's father entered the room; Joseph Jackson turned quickly away from the window, so that he would not be tempted to look through the magic bubble until his father's inspection was finished. John Lister was quite strict with his only son, who had come to him when he had given up hoping for a boy, almost twenty years after the birth of Joseph Jackson's two sisters.

"All finished with thy task?" John Lister asked.

"Yes, Father," Joseph Jackson answered, handing the copybook over.

"It is well done, in the allotted time," his father pronounced at last. "There should be no more complaints from thy school about slowness, and no more plum cakes withheld on that account! And, even more important, I am beginning to think we need no longer fear that thee has any traces of thy Cousin Steven's slothful disposition, which caused him to lie abed and come late to meals, so I could no longer keep him in my house."